Mo.
Bryony Lavery

Bryony Lavery is a playwright, director, performer and teacher of playwriting. Her plays include *Bag, Flight, Two Marias, Wicked, Origin of the Species, Witchcraze, Calamity, Kitchen Matters* and the award-winning *Her Aching Heart*. She has been writer in residence at the Unicorn Theatre for Children and was one of the Artistic Directors for Gay Sweatshop.

CONNECTIONS

More Light
BRYONY LAVERY

ff

faber and faber

STANLEY
THORNES

First published in this edition 2001
by Faber and Faber Limited
3 Queen Square London WC1N3AU
Published in the United States by Faber and Faber, Inc.,
an affiliate of Farrar, Straus and Giroux, New York
More Light was first published in *New Connections*, 1997

Typeset by Parker Typesetting Service, Leicester
Printed in England by Mackays of Chatham PLC, Chatham, Kent

A CIP record for this book
is available from the British Library

ISBN 0-571-20691-3 (Faber edn)
ISBN 0-7487-4287-5 (Stanley Thornes edn)

2 4 6 8 10 9 7 5 3 1

Contents

Foreword

The plays in this series were generated through a unique and epic project initiated by the Royal National Theatre, London, and funded by BT.

 For many years the Education Department at the RNT had been receiving calls from youth theatre companies and schools asking us to recommend scripts for them to perform. They were looking for contemporary, sophisticated, unpatronising scripts with great plots and storylines, where the characters would fit the age range of the young people playing them. At that time, there weren't many plays written for the 11-to-19 age group. So we decided to approach the best writing talent around and ask them to write short plays specifically for young people.

 In two-year cycles over a period of six years, we created a portfolio of new plays and invited 150 schools and youth theatres to choose the one that most excited them. We then invited the participants to come on a weekend retreat and work through the script with the writer before producing the play in their home venue. Some of those productions were then invited to one of ten festivals at professional theatres throughout the UK. Each two-year cycle culminated in a summer festival at the Royal National Theatre, where the stages, back-stage areas and foyers were ablaze with youthful energy and creativity.

 But the story doesn't end there. As we've discovered, the UK isn't alone in demanding fantastic new scripts for the youth market. A fourth cycle is already under way and this time the portfolio will include more contributions from overseas. As long as there's a need, we will continue to commission challenging work to feed the intelligence, imagination and ingenuity of young people and the adults with whom they work.

Suzy Graham-Adriani
Royal National Theatre
July 2000

For more information on the writers and the work involved on the BT/National Connections project, visit: www.nt-online.org

MORE LIGHT

Bryony Lavery

Characters

The ladies of the Emperor:
More Light
Love's Gift
Young Friend
Fresh Morning
Many Treasures
Rapture
Sparkling Eyes
Moist Moss
Playful Kitten
Scent-of-Ginger
Shy Smile
Love Mouth
Pure Heart
Pure Mind
Pure Joy
Perfect Pleasure

Man, a convict
Modern Man
Modern Woman

Act One

SCENE ONE   THE DARK AGES

There is darkness.
There is the sound of wooden chimes blowing in the
wind. A single, nearer sound, as of a tinder box struck.
A small light appears.
We smell sandalwood incense.
The light picks out the face of a young woman. She is
dressed in an enveloping black cloak, but we cannot see
this. All we see is a whitened face, eyes, a red mouth. She
speaks.

Woman
In the twentieth year of his rule
the all-powerful Emperor
now in sight of Death's gates
gave thought to the construction of his tomb . . .
To the high-ceilinged palace
were admitted
mathematicians   astrologers   metalsmiths
artists   architects   inventors.
Each put the most splendid workings
of his mind upon paper
and rolled out the paper
so that covering the Emperor's tables
was the most splendid Art
of the most splendid minds
in The Empire.
And soon, in his all-powerful mind,
the Emperor saw his tomb.

A sound of galloping hoofs.

Leaving the palace at dawn
with only four soldiers
he mounted his horse and rode east.
At dusk,
having ridden all day, he stopped,
dismounted and said,
'Here is where my tomb shall be.'
And so it was
for the Empire was his
and the gentle hill on which he stood
was his
and the red sun which lit the hill
was his.
The four soldiers marked the place.

In the high-ceilinged palace
on his return
the all-powerful Emperor
summoned one of his Guard.
The Guard moved silently through
the sleeping palace.

She listens.
    Four screams fill the air.

As the sun rose
four soldiers in the palace did not.
The punishment for this infringement of
rules
is flogging.
This did not greatly trouble the four
soldiers,
now in Death's kingdom.

Some miles off from the gentle hill
a tunnel was started.

The tunnel,
dug day and night by the Emperor's
convicts,
approached the hill.

The Emperor,
his body now frail
but his all-powerful mind not,
entered the twenty-first year of his rule.
There were many celebrations.

Fireworks briefly illuminate the space.

The tunnel reached the hill.
It was wide and high.
The Emperor's convicts worked and slept
in the tunnel.
The smell of their bodies
was wide and high.

In the light of many lanterns
the hill was hollowed out.
Above spring turned to summer
autumn to winter
day to night.

Beneath the hill
it was always day
for the work was continuous
and it was always night
for it was always dark.

The cavern
they hollowed out
was enormous.

Mathematicians   astrologers   metalsmiths
architects   inventors
rode on horses along the wide high tunnel

into the hill.
They dismounted
and with their Art
began to prepare the tomb.

The tomb was like this.
Such Art!
The ceiling was the night sky
above the Empire.
Artists painted it the deepest blue.
Their arms ached with the work.
Every star was in its place,
a jewel cut and set by the most precise
of jewellers.
The floor was the map of the Empire,
fields, woods, houses, roads, the skill of
gold and silversmiths,
the three mighty rivers
made, in this tomb,
from quicksilver,
dry to the touch
and flowing from source to end
by the art of engineers.

Three gates there were to the tomb
set within three walls.
Mounted at each gate
was a pair of mechanical archers.
Anyone entering these gates
uninvited
into the tomb of the Emperor
would be shot with silver arrows.
Such Art!

In the centre
beyond the third gate
was the entire army of the Empire

cast in bronze
with which the Emperor
would fight his enemies
in the realms of Death.

In truth
the Emperor's tomb
was the most splendid
of all the wonders accomplished in his
rule.

The Emperor
now with one hand knocking at Death's door
said,
'So that my tomb
may be my final resting place
and so that my body
will not be disturbed,
let it be made clear
that all those who have worked on this
tomb
shall die with me.
They shall stay in the tomb,
the gates will be locked,
the entrance sealed
and no one on this earth
will know where my tomb is.
This Art will survive in perfection.
And I will be as inviolate in death
as I was in life.'

A bell starts tolling far away.

So it was
that at the outer wall
stood the Emperor's convicts,
at the middle wall
stood

architects   astrologers   metalsmiths
artists   architects   inventors,
the most special minds in the Empire.

The Emperor
now with both hands
pulled at Death's doors
and they parted.

'Take me to my tomb,'
he said.
And the ones so honoured to escort
the Emperor
on his last journey
were those of his ladies
who had borne him no son
and were to tend his body
within the inner gate.

The Emperor walked through Death's doors.
'More light,' he said,
and his ladies
held lanterns close to his body,
but he did not see,
for Death's doors had closed upon him.

And so it was,
walking beside a dead man,
my hands burning from the lantern,
I,
one of his ladies
who had borne him no sons,
entered the tomb.

Many lanterns provide more light.
    *The woman takes off her dark cloak. She is wearing a
magnificent eastern gown, lacquered wig, white powder,
high platforms supporting bound feet. Her name is
More Light.*

SCENE TWO   MORE LIGHT

More Light
    I have had a most wonderful life.
    I have known only the finest of food.
    I have slept on the softest sheets.
    I have known only the Emperor.
    My garden has been green.

    I walked the wide road to the tomb
    ready to serve my Emperor.

    Death is an honour
    in such company.

    The wide road came to an end.
    Our procession stood at the outer gate.
    It opened.

    She takes out a fan.

    Such heat.

    She opens her fan.

    Such a smell of unclean bodies.

    She uses her fan to waft the air. She is short of breath.

    I lower my eyes.

    She lowers her eyelids modestly. Her fan covers her face
    but not her eyes.

    Saw this way and this way
    shapes, men, eyes watching.
    The Convicts I think.

    Her eyes dart and sidle.
    We pass through the outer gate –
    it closes.

She is more breathless.

Our procession at the middle gate.
More heat still.
Men stand
looking.
I lower my eyes.
Put up my fan.
The most special minds of the Empire
mathematicians   astrologers   metalsmiths
artists   architects   inventors
eyes watching.
Men I think.
So
the middle gate
opens,
closes.

Her eyes fix on something ahead. It is horrible.

Our procession
at an end
at an end
at the inner gate.

It opens,
it closes
for ever.

She looks towards us. Her eyes are blank and dark.

My garden has been green.
My face is white.
Inside my head it is black, it is black,
it is black.
I am twenty years old.

*Everything goes black. She screams and screams and
screams.*

Light returns suddenly.
    A screen or curtain has been removed and sitting in a row, in the inner gate, are the Emperor's ladies who have borne him no sons. They are of all ages, from sixty down to six. They are all dressed as concubines, ladies of the court, wealthy whores . . . there are countless examples in the different periods of art to choose from.
    They are all painted with white paint. More Light sits with them. They will sit quietly like this for as long as possible. When it becomes unbearable, More Light speaks.

More Light
    No one has spoken
    since the Emperor died.
    All of us women sit in silence,
    backs straight,

Some backs are straightened.

hands still.

One pair of hands flutters and is still.

What to do

Their faces express apathy.

but sit and die
with our Emperor?

They sit still for another long time.

We are hungry.
We are thirsty.
What shall we do?
We have known only the finest of food.
We have slept on the softest sheets.

Our garden has been green.
We have known only the Emperor

All eyes look modestly down.

and now his soul lives behind
Death's doors
and we sit before them,
our minds on his empty body.
What shall we do?

I look at them,
the Emperor's ladies
who have borne him no sons.

She names them. Each one makes a small, precise
acknowledgement of her name.

Love's Gift
Young Friend
Fresh Morning
Many Treasures
Rapture
Sparkling Eyes
Moist Moss
Playful Kitten
Scent-of-Ginger
Shy Smile
Love Mouth
Pure Heart
Pure Mind
Pure Joy
Perfect Pleasure

They all start to piteously rock

Piteously they rock.
What shall we do?

SCENE FOUR   A BIRD IDEA

More Light
My mind washes.
I am in fresh air.

Wind blows. It is cold and fresh. More Light takes a
sheet of paper. She proceeds to make an origami bird as
she reveals the image in her mind.

I see an egg
in a nest
on a cliff
above the sea,
although I have never in my short life seen
a sea.
I hear a 'chip chip'.
A small hole appears in the brown-speckled
shell.
A beak.
An ugly damp matty head appears.
An ugly damp matty bird falls from the
broken shell.
It dries in the sun.
It grooms itself.
It is sleek, it has feathers, it has wings.
It stretches and launches itself over the
cliff.
It drops.
It steadies itself on the air
and then it flies
up into the wind,
up into the sky.
The sun warms it.

The bird is now constructed.

I look at the ladies.
Piteously they wail . . .

The ladies wail.

Eat him
I say.

SCENE FIVE   MORE BIRDS MAKE A FLOCK

The ladies all stop wailing at once.

More Light
Eat him
I say.

The ladies' eyes go round. Their mouths open in an 'O'.

Each painted red mouth
in each white-painted face opens.
He is our Emperor.
He has always fed us.
He would not want us to go hungry.
Let us eat him.

Each lady takes a sheet of paper and constructs an origami bird. They are considering the proposition.

If we leave him too long
he will not be fresh

and we have known only the
finest of food.

More Light is playing with her paper bird.

The most special of dishes.

The finest cuts of meat.

We have always eaten royally.

I am so hungry.

What else is there to eat?

There is silence. The ladies finish their birds. They contemplate them.

There is silence.
All eyes look down modestly.
Then
one red mouth opens.

A lady's mouth opens.

Love's Gift . . .?
Love's Gift Sister, how shall it be done?

A great sound of birds' wings flapping. If only the paper birds could fly away in a great white flock, this would be wonderful.

SCENE SIX   THE ROYAL ARMY PROTECTS AND
SUCCOURS ITS LADIES

More Light puts an elegant finger to her chin to ponder the question. She walks a little. The ladies watch with rapt interest.

More Light Ah!
Ladies Aaaaaah!
More Light
Perhaps we can borrow some
utensils
from the Emperor's own bronze army
of death?

Stirring, impressive, solemn martial music. The ladies

remove a screen, revealing the head of a phalanx of
bronze military figures.

Each bronze warrior stands
his bronze weapon in his bronze grip.
The entire army of the Emperor,
each face individual,
each belt fastening,
each link of chain mail lovingly wrought.
Such Art!
I take a bronze sword.

She does.

Pure Heart takes a bronze dagger.

Pure Heart does.

Pure Mind takes a bronze axe.

Pure Mind does.

Pure Joy takes a bronze helmet.

Pure Joy does.
   They return the screen. As they do, they hear the
sound of men's voices.
   More Light continues in a whisper.

At the wall we hear
   a voice, many voices . . .
Voices
   Who is that?
   What is happening?
   What is going on?
   Have you food?

The ladies freeze.

More Light (*still in a whisper, this time informative*)
the mathematicians   astrologers
    metalsmiths   artists   architects   inventors
    the most special minds in the Empire.

The ladies are impressed.

We say nothing.
We, the Emperor's ladies,
speak to no man but
the Emperor.

All ladies are in full agreement here.

SCENE SEVEN   THE EMPEROR

*The ladies remove another screen and there, lying in state
on a bed, is the Emperor.*

More Light
    The Emperor lies asleep
    in Death's arms.
    The ladies of the Emperor
    remark on his deathly form.
Rapture How still he is!
More Light Rapture gazes.
Moist Moss How blue-white his skin.
More Light Moist Moss touches his cheek.
Shy Smile How cold he is.
More Light Shy Smile touches his hand.
Perfect Pleasure How fat he is.
More Light
    Perfect Pleasure lays both hands
        upon his richly embroidered chest.
Perfect Pleasure Sister . . . how is it to be done?

More Light

All eyes, all white faces, all round
red mouths turn to me.

They do.

Take off his clothes.

As they do, More Light contemplates.

We have undressed for our Emperor
many times.
He sat on cushions of silk
as we unwound our sashes,
opened our robes,
stepped down from our shoes,
rolled our white stockings down past
our knees, over our ankles, off our toes,
one by one
unpinned our hair
and combed it with our fingers
down over our marble breasts.
His eyes followed our every move.
Now we undress him.
Fresh Morning unfastens the row of
pearl buttons
on his embroidered coat.
She works from neckband to hem.
Her fabled fingers fly.
Moist Moss and Scent-of-Ginger shell the
Emperor of his coat.
He is very stiff.
Their celebrated strength succeeds.
Little Friend takes off his jewelled shoes,
his white socks off his toes,
one by one.
Pure Heart, Pure Mind, Pure Joy

ease off his silk trousers.
The Emperor lies naked
but for his golden war helmet.

The ladies put up their fans to hide their faces. More
Light stares at the Emperor.

I have never
looked at him like this.
He has always looked at me!

She puts up her fan. The ladies simultaneously bring
theirs down.

Ladies
I have had no joy of
the Emperor.
He lay on his bed.
I stood at the foot.
He stared at my face.
Two girls,
thirteen years old,
pour oil on to their hands,

Dance with their hands.

Anoint his loins.
Such art.
Mould with the hands,
shape with the hands,
the soft, soft clay there
into something,
caressing, kneading, moving, shaping,
sculpturing,
turning soft clay
firing soft clay,
into hard, firm, erect Male Figure Sculpture.
I crawl from the foot of the bed
on hands and knees,

Round Female Sculpture.
The two girls help me,
help the two sculpture figures,
become one.
I am hard dry clay.
Ah Ah Ah.
Art is Pain.
I feel a hand over my face,
the hand of the Emperor.
It turns my head,
turns the Female Sculpture
through ninety degrees.
Ah Ah Ah
Art again   Pain again.
I make no sound.
My face shows pleasure.

Many Treasures Sister . . . we have taken off his clothes . . .

Playful Kitten Apart from his golden helmet . . .

Rapture Dead as dead . . .

Love Mouth In his huge golden war helmet . . .

Sparkling Eyes Naked as naked . . .

Playful Kitten With his small white love-member . . .

They put up their fans. We hear a giggle. Fans start to shake. One by one the fans come down and everyone is grinning, then giggling, then chortling, then laughing . . . They try to show respect for a while. They fail. They fall about, hit each other, cry with laughter. More Lights lowers her fan and watches.

More Light
This is what they fear . . .
those who hold empires
that we will look and really see.
The Emperor is dead.

SCENE EIGHT   SEVERING THE PAST

More Light I lift up the bronze sword.

She does.
  The ladies fall back.

The ladies melt back into the gloom.
I stand before my Emperor.
I use all my strength.
The sword goes 'clish' in the air
and I slice through his left shoulder
clear to the bone.

The ladies gasp and ululate.

A thick line appears in the skin,
the flesh parts.
My mouth is dry.
Rapture
  Sister,
  the limb is not cut through . . .
  Perhaps if we bend back the arm
  we might sever the tendons
  as one might snap off a chicken wing . . .
More Light
  Fresh Morning and Many Treasures
  take the arm.
  They twist it.
  Then there is a sound worse than any
  I have heard . . .

The ladies keen.

It is the shoulder socket dislocating.
I lift the sword again,
'clish' the blade arcs down,
and the Emperor's arm drops to the floor.

Moist Moss Oh, sister . . . it is done.

She pats More Light's sword arm.

Many Treasures Hard work . . . butchering.
Playful Kitten What a lot of flesh on a man's arm . . .

She examines the shoulder.

Perfect Pleasure I am so hungry!

She kneels on the floor.

Love Mouth (*pouting*)
  But . . . raw meat . . . my
  stomach is too delicate for raw meat . . .
Shy Smile
  Look . . . the lanterns . . . they still
  burn . . . perhaps . . . if we made a fire . . .
  we might roast the Emperor's arm . . .

A sound of a fire crackling. It roars. The area is suffused with flame red. Then darkness.

SCENE NINE   MANY TREASURES

Light up on Many Treasures.

Many Treasures
  The Emperor's arm tastes
  of venison.

This is all very new and interesting. Many Treasures is interested in the art of cooking.

  Slightly gamy with a suggestion of salt.
  I think we roasted the arm too quickly . . .
  the outside was scorched
  and the meat nearest the bone too raw.

Our cooking improved.
The ladies of the Emperor are noted for
their quickness.
Their brains are not softened by
child-bearing.
His legs tasted of roast pork!
His ribs of beef.
His feet of duck.
His innards made a fine stew,
thick, good gravy, with many tasty lumps.
His member was soft and tasted of cheese,
but we all knew that,
for many of us
had tasted it before.
The Emperor
with his fine strong body
shields us from death for many days.
The Emperor protects us
in death
as he did in life.

SCENE TEN   MORE LIGHT EXAMINES
SCULPTURE

*Lights up on More Light, alone among the bronze army. She
is contemplating the figure of a soldier. She looks at its
forthright stance, its open face, and compares it with herself.*

More Light
The inner gate is strewn with bones.
The air smells of cooked meat and
tallow grease.
The ladies' faces are no longer white.
The red paint is gone from the mouths.
The skin is dank, yellow and smutted.

Our bellies are round and full
as if we bear sons.

*She strokes the face of the warrior. Then his chest, then
his legs, then his feet.*
 Various ladies appear.

Love Mouth Sister . . . the Emperor is almost gone.

She nibbles a fingerbone.

Smell-of-Ginger Sister . . . the Emperor is almost used up.

She scrapes a piece of skin.

Pure Mind Sister, the Emperor can no longer
Pure Heart Provide for us.
Pure Joy What is to be done?

More Light thinks.
 The various ladies think.

More Light
 Our brains are small,

This is demonstrable from the bronze warrior.

unused but for pleasure pastimes.
For help in this most difficult
problem we must look to the most special
workings
of the most special minds in
the Empire . . .
Love Mouth the mathematicians
Scent-of-Ginger astrologers
Pure Mind metalsmiths
Pure Heart artists   architects
Pure Joy inventors
More Light Who occupy the middle gate.

All faces turn to the wall. They listen.

Love Mouth (*quietly*) We have heard voices,
Scent-of-Ginger the sounds of motion,
Pure Mind cries even,
Pure Heart but it is not our practice to talk with other men.
Pure Joy We ladies talk only to the Emperor!

They tiptoe to the wall screen. They listen.
    All is silent.
    They all whisper.

Love Mouth Nothing.
Scent-of-Ginger Perhaps they are all asleep.
Pure Mind Perhaps they are all weak with hunger!
Pure Heart Perhaps they are all dead . . .
Pure Joy For they have not had the protection of the Emperor!

They listen.

More Light There is no sound beyond the wall.

More whispered conference.

Love Mouth
    If they are all dead
    we must collect them and cook them.
Scent-of-Ginger Pickle them!
Love Mouth Before they go off!
Scent-of-Ginger Ay . . . what a waste of meat!
Pure Mind
    We must find out the state of matters
    beyond the middle wall!
Pure Heart Sister . . .

They all turn to More Light.

Pure Joy What is to be done?
More Light We must prepare!

*The ladies watch as she starts to remove her high-heeled
shoes. She makes her clothes comfortable.*

*The ladies understand. They remove restricting
garments – corsets, restraining bodices, tight unbendable
sleeves.*

*They borrow pieces as needed from the bronze army.
They start to move, then almost dance, in a much freer,
more open way.*

*They hear chinking and clanking. It is their jewellery
– bangles, necklaces, earrings and rings. They remove
them.*

Pure Joy How well we move!
Pure Heart How free!
Pure Mind How light!!!
All three Sister, what is to be done?
More Light
We must open the door
and take a peep!
Ladies Yes!
Pure Joy
Ayee . . . but the mechanical archers!
They will fire on us!
Ladies Ayee!
More Light
No . . . no!
The mechanical archers
fire out
not in!
Love Mouth They will fire upon the mathematicians
Scent-of-Ginger astrologers
Pure Mind metalsmiths   artists
Pure Heart architects   inventors
Pure Joy all the most special minds in the Empire . . .
More Light who Built This Tomb!

SCENE ELEVEN   OPENING THE GATES OF KNOWLEDGE

More Light
  Take hold of the left handle,
  Pure Mind.
Pure Mind Yes.
More Light
  Take hold of the right,
  Pure Heart.
Pure Heart Yes.
Pure Joy Now!

*They open the gates. There is the sound of mighty
doors opening in a vast building.*
  *All the present ladies follow More Light through the
gates.*
  *Pure Joy remains with us. She is well mannered and
loves beauty, so she describes the gate screen to us.*

The gates in the middle wall
are exquisite,
of beaten gold and silver.
They bear pictures of the triumphs
of the Emperor's rule.

*A sound rends the air. Two arrows travelling at speed.
Then silence.*
  *Pure Joy gasps with fear and clutches her heart. She
listens. Nothing. She continues to entertain us.*

Of beaten gold and silver,
they bear pictures of the triumphs
of the Emperor's rule.

She loves detail.

Here is his army victorious in battle,

here are his road-builders reaching the
farthest outposts of the Empire,
here are his tax collectors in a small
village collecting corn,
here is a thief, having his hand cut off,
here are his stonemasons building a
great wall in the north.
Around the gate handles
choirs sing praises
and hosts pray.

There is a knocking at the gate.

Who is it?

From behind the gates.

More Light Open the gates, Fool!

*Pure Joy abases herself for us at More Light's rudeness
as she opens the gates.*
    *Another sound of two arrows travelling at speed. The
sound of muffled screams from behind the gates.*
    *The party of ladies appears, dragging or carrying two
men sitting bound and cross-legged, their mouths oddly
full and each with staring eyes and arrows embedded in
their hearts.*

Shut the gates, Fool!

*More abasement from Pure Joy for More Light's
rudeness as she shuts the gates.*

Scent-of-Ginger My heart pounds!
Love Mouth My mouth! Dry!
Pure Mind My palms! Moist!
Pure Heart I have wet myself!

    Pure Joy abases herself.

Ladies Oh oh oh oh oh!!!!

They scream.

More Light
Quiet, fools!
My head is full with your wailing.
I need to think!

They are silent at her fierceness.
She kneels down before one of the corpses.

This was Clever Hands
the inventor.
He it was who made the water flow
upwards to the higher fields.
He it was who made the device which
turned the ox carcass so that it
roasted evenly.
He it was who made the mechanical
singing linnet for the Emperor's
third son.
He it was who made the mechanical
archer which has now shot him
through the heart.
Love Mouth Sister . . . we are all hungry . . .
Scent-of-Ginger
Sister . . . we must attend to him
before he goes off . . .
More Light
Who bound his arms and legs?

She feels in his mouth, takes out rags.

Who gagged him?
Love Mouth (*to Pure Joy*) Make sure the gates are secure.
Scent-of-Ginger The important thing is to eat!

Pure Mind, Pure Heart, Love Mouth and Scent-of-
Ginger take the bodies away to the other ladies.

See what we have found!
Many Treasures Ayee!
Love Mouth An inventor!
Playful Kitten This is Sees Future, the astrologer!
Many Treasures
    Thinner than the Emperor
    leaner flesh
    tougher
    more consistent of texture . . .
    Careful braising I think . . .

*They take the corpses behind a screen. There are the
shadows of swords raised, the sound of dismembering.*

SCENE TWELVE   THE MIDDLE GATE

Pure Joy
    It is written
    in works of astrology
    that the astrologer can foretell
    everyone's future
    but his own.
More Light
    Beyond the gates there
    we peered into the blackness.
    All is silent.
    But no . . . we hear breathing.
    Love Mouth lifts the lantern.

    Everywhere
    eyes
    low
    staring up at us,
    row upon row of eyes
    staring out from the most special minds

of the Empire.
Their feet and hands
are bound.
Their mouths stuffed with rags.
Two move not at all.
Arrows in their hearts.
'Take these two,'
I hear a voice say.
The ladies look at me.
It is my voice.
They move along the seated trussed men
the most special minds of the Empire
and drag away the two carcasses
across the floor
and through the gate
to eat.
What of our future?

Pure Joy Sister, we are in a tomb.

SCENE THIRTEEN   A MEAL

*Many Treasures brings on a steaming cauldron. The ladies
coo and flutter with pleasure. They line up, each with a
bronze helmet. Many Treasures ladles steaming stew into
each one.*

Love's Gift I have a little more than my sister.
Fresh Morning Ah no. I am happy.
Rapture
   Little Friend is still growing . . .
   Perhaps another spoonful?
Sparkling Eyes How carefully cut is the meat!
Many Treasures
   The size of a walnut.
   The best size.

Rapture
  Little Friend . . . Playful Kitten . . .
  take the soft place.
Scent-of-Ginger Heaven in the mouth!
Many Treasures Not too melting?
Ladies
  No, no.
  Not too melting at all!

Pure Joy and More Light enter.

Many Treasures Casserole, dear sisters?
Pure Joy Aaah!

*Playful Kitten gives her helmet of stew to More Light,
then goes and lays her head in Rapture's lap. Playful
Kitten is very young.*

More Light This is yours, Playful Kitten.
Rapture You must eat, little sister.
Many Treasures
  Perhaps cut up the pieces to
  pistachio size, sister?
Playful Kitten It makes me dream.
Rapture What does it make you dream, little one?
Playful Kitten Bad things.
Rapture What bad things, little one?
Playful Kitten
  I become a big bad thing
  and I roar
  and I stand in the dark
  and my chin is hair
  and my eyes look at me
  and want to watch me all
  the while
  and I hurt between my legs.

She puts her face to Rapture's lap.

32

The ladies have stopped eating.

Rapture I have this dream too, little sister.

She strokes her head.

Love Mouth I too.

The other ladies nod.
Love Mouth addresses Many Treasures.

It is no criticism of your cooking!
Ladies No! Oh no, no!
Love Mouth We are simply doing wrong.
Ladies Yes! Oh yes!
More Light (*laughs*)
Yes!
We are the ladies of the Emperor!
We are here on this earth to serve
the Emperor . . .
to please him
to amuse him
to bear him sons!
But we have not borne him sons . . .
So we must serve him in other ways!
How?
Let us go with him through Death's doors!
Yes!
Let us walk with him!
But wait!
Where is he?
Where is he, Playful Kitten?
Playful Kitten We ate him, More Light.
More Light
We ate him!
He was good to us, Playful Kitten . . .
better than he knew!
For he is now in us!

33

He occupies our bellies
as if he had given us sons!
We have his dreams!
Ladies, we are now all . . . all . . .
Emperor of all we survey!

The ladies ponder this.

Pure Joy
It is written
in studies of other religions
of a religion whose devotees
eat of the body of their god
and drink of his blood
and their god lives in them.
More Light
I am Emperor here.
I believe this is possible.
Playful Kitten, do you believe
this also?
Little Goddess.
Child Emperor.

More Light abases herself before Playful Kitten.

Playful Kitten Yes!
(*imperiously*) Hand me my helmet!
Many Treasures (*equally imperiously*) More casserole!

The ladies resume eating.

Pure Joy (*thoughtfully contemplating her casserole*)
If it is true that we are all now
the Emperor
for he is now one with us

All ladies nod.

by the same token
we must all be

34

She takes a mouthful.

inventors

She takes another mouthful.

astrologers
for they too
are now one with us.
More Light What of our future, sister?
Pure Joy
Let us have one, sister!
Let us be Emperors of our world.
Let us be its
mathematicians astrologers metalsmiths
artists inventors
architects.
As the Emperor constructed his tomb
so let us construct our world!

*The ladies dress Playful Kitten in the dead Emperor's
clothes.*

Playful Kitten It's a game?
Pure Joy It's a game!
Playful Kitten I'm an Emperor!

SCENE FOURTEEN   THE EARLY RENAISSANCE

More Light
In the first year of her rule
the all-powerful Emperor
now in sight of Death's gates
gave thought to the construction of her
world . . .
to the high-ceilinged tomb
were admitted

mathematicians   astrologers   metalsmiths
artists   inventors   architects.
Each put the most splendid workings
of her mind upon paper
and rolled out the paper
so that covering the Emperor's tables
was the most splendid Art
of the most splendid minds
in the Empire.
And soon, in her all-powerful mind,
the Emperor saw her world.

*The ladies, who have adopted new attitudes as the
Emperors and the most splendid minds in the Empire,
contemplate their world.*

SCENE FIFTEEN   THE EMPEROR LEAVES HIS
PALACE

Pure Joy Such Art, sister.
More Light What else have we?
Many Treasures
  Sister . . . a word.
  The inventor is on his last legs . . .
  Someone must go beyond the gate.
More Light Why me?
Many Treasures
  The ladies are occupied.
  constructing . . . inventing . . .
Pure Joy
  You are our Empire's sword.
  Without this our world is threatened.
More Light
  I have had a most wonderful life.

I have known only the finest of food.
I have slept on the softest of sheets.
I have known only the Emperor.
My garden has been green.
Pure Joy I will open the gate.
More Light
My voice is no longer low and melodious.
It is harsh as a sword stroke.

More Light takes a sword.
   The gates are opened by Pure Joy.
   We hear the sound of two arrows through the air.
   More Light walks into blackness.

I can see nothing!
Fool!
I search with my hand out in front
of me for dead men.

A sharp intake of breath.

I smell a wide, high smell!
There is something here.

We hear women's voices ululating.

I light my lamp.

*She lights her lamp. Light reveals her standing with her
back to us. Projected is the shadow of a huge man.*

Aaagh!

The man's arm rises. It holds an axe.
   More Light turns round.

Aaagh!
Standing before me,
an axe in his hand,
is a man.

The axe is raised.
It is made of bone!

The light comes up to reveal exactly that.
   Furious drumming. Women wailing. Then darkness.

Act Two

SCENE ONE   PURE JOY OF ART

A sound of something musical, between a xylophone and a celeste. The notes are tentative, exploratory.
  The lights reveal Scent-of-Ginger among the bronze army. She tries out notes on various bits of the bronze soldiers.

Scent-of-Ginger
  Tsk!
  Ah!
  Bah!
  They are so out of tune!

She takes out a percussion instrument composed of hung helmets, daggers, belt buckles etc. She plays a melody on them.

  Hmm.
  Yes.
  I see . . .
  It all needs rearranging!

Nearer, lights reveal some of the ladies posing. Above them is a mobile of origami birds.
  Love Mouth is sketching them.

Pure Joy
  Love Mouth draws us all for a
  composite group portrait.
Love Mouth Don't move.
Pure Joy
  None of us is moving.
  Trained only for politeness,

39

respect and servitude,
we struggle like crawling toddlers
towards the skills of creation.

Love Mouth Daaghhh!

Pure Joy

I find myself the stillest of us
all for I am thinking.
What art?
Hundreds of years hence
people will penetrate this tomb
and they will see the painted sky
studded with jewelled stars,
the rivers of quicksilver,
the mechanical archers,
the gates,
the bronze army,
and say,
'Look, it is the sky,
the stars, the rivers, archers,
the gates, and that must be
the army!
What Art!
And look, in this middle section here,
these skeletons, wrapped in fine clothes,
these must the women!
What were they doing here?'

Love Mouth Keep still!

Pure Joy

And one of them, keener-eyed than
the rest, may find, among the dust,
the shape of a bird,
and he will touch it
and the old old paper bird will
fall to dust,
and he will say,
'No, I was mistaken.

it is nothing,'
and will turn back to the beautiful
gold and silver gate.

Love Mouth
Hold your heads a little more . . .

They all hold their heads a little more . . .

Yes, that's pretty, yes.

Pure Joy
So I keep still,
while my eyes and mind scamper and
scrape like a rat about this monument,
looking,
looking for the post and lintel
on which to rest the architecture
of my dis-ease,
for the arch to take the weight
of my fear,
for the rib vaults and flying buttresses
to hurl my hope stone-like
into the ether.

Love Mouth
If you want to be part of my
picture, sister . . .
you must Keep Still!

Pure Joy keeps still.
  Love Mouth sketches.

I am going to put us all
in the palace garden.
With the sun coming through the trees.
Flowers in the grass in the foreground.
A table with food.
Dew-dropped fruit.

Red wine in a glass flagon.
In the background the village
of my childhood just under
the mountains.
An early evening sky.
And we will all be smiling
in delight!

Phhh!
Well . . . rest a while.

Love Mouth contemplates her work furiously.
Pure Joy rises.

Pure Joy
There are no flowers here.
No sun.
But I remember.
Do I make flowers?
We are in a tomb?
Do I show Death?
We are in a hell.
Do I create hell?
We construct a world.
Do I show hope?
What colour is hope?

Playful Kitten and Little Friend run on. They have tied
long ribbons to the end of bronze daggers. They play
with them, slashing the air with random trickles and
blazes of colour. They run off.
    Pure Joy starts moving in time with the melody of
Many Treasures. She adopts a strong pose.

You remember that statue in the
Great Hall?

She slightly alters her pose.

The beautiful young man?
Walking forward.
into the future.
The Kouros.
Feet planted firmly on the earth.
Strong limbs.
Striding forward.
Head high and proud!

All the women adopt the strong pose.

We thought him splendid!

Love Mouth
Oh, that is new!
I need *more light*!

The lights fade.

SCENE TWO   ADAM AND EVE

*Lights up on the second gate. More Light, bound and
gagged, is hurled in by a Man, wild and hairy, who sports
a recent sword gash. He carries an axe of bone and a
bronze sword.*

Man
Can't run much, Royal Shag!
Can't run at all now!
Can't screech now, Palace Parrot!
Nice piece o' work this!

Indicates sword.

Nice piece o' work this!

Indicates sword gash.

43

Do it ta you now, eh?
Bleed blue, willya?
Cut off a wing, eh?
Taste of parrot, willya?
I've ett of the smart boys thought up this cage.
Tasted of paper and books.
Gotta taste for bird.
Eaten raw fowl before.
How I got penned in this hutch
For that big misdemeanour,
stealing food.
Mebbe make a big fire
Have
Sunday roast.
Right royal feast you'd be
Parrot.
Na . . . gonna take the stuffing outta
your crop, Polly . . .
an' ya gonna say who's a Pretty
Boy then to me
an' no screeching or your blue
parrot tongue's Pretty Boy's
first bite, am I clear?
Nod your head if you're a
talking bird!

More Light nods her head.
   He takes out the gag.
   She chokes and gags.

Too much dry corn, Poll.

He gives her water to drink from his hip flagon.

'Ave some pure fresh rainwater.
Courtesy the lads on the outer
gate.

Comes through the walls.
Very tasty tomb with running water
we got.
'Spect you're sipping purified silver
in the middle there?
Let's you and me talk, Parrot.
Emperor dead yet?
More Light Yes.
Man Yessss!

He smites the air.

And maggots forever bite and chew
his fat carcass!
Yessss!
Fat bastard took along a flock
of you parrots.
Wass happened to them?
More Light
Dead.
Every one.
Man
Every one but you, Poll.
How comes you still fluttering?
More Light Same way as you, convict.
Man You ett bird?
More Light I ate bird.
Man
Yessss!
What it taste like?
Sweet?
Soft?
Chicken?
More Light
Sweet.
Soft.
Chicken.

45

Yes.

Man

Like that, me.

Like a taste of that.

More Light

But you can't taste that, convict.

It is all gone.

Man Part from this, Poll.

He touches her.

More Light

Apart from this, convict.

Emperor's Parrot.

Whose voice sung him melodies.

Whose tongue caressed his ear.

Only the best for the Emperor.

Finest, softest of voices

talking to him only of pleasure

in his ear,

lips murmuring on his ear

of pleasure.

Man

Emperor's woman.

Say what you did.

He puts his ear to her mouth.

More Light (*in a whisper*)

I gave him pleasure.

Only the best for the Emperor.

The most practised of touches.

The most elegant of movements.

The deepest of knowledge in how

to show the Emperor love.

Man

Show me, woman.

I'm Emperor here now.

46

More Light Unbind me then, my lord.
Man What am I, a fool?
More Light Yes.
Man You're dead.
More Light You also, Fool.
Man

> Then I'll go like an Emperor.
> Die of pleasure from a
> bird of paradise pecking
> and feathers.

He unties her.

> Show me the art of love,
> Parrot.
> I'm the Emperor.

More Light

> He lies in his bed.
> I stand at the foot.
> He looks into my face.
> I lower my eyes modestly
> behind my fan.
> Two girls,
> thirteen years old,
> pour oil on to their hands,

She performs all this for him.

> anoint his body,

She begins to stroke him.

> take away all his cares,

*She places the bronze sword and bone axe carefully,
usefully for her. He watches.*

> anoints his head, his neck,
> his shoulders stiff from battle,

47

She puts her hand inside his shirt.

his manly chest.
He has no breasts.
Anoints his thighs, his loins.
Such Art.
Mould with the hands,
shape with the hands,
the soft, soft clay there
into something
caressing, kneading, moving, shaping,
sculpturing,
turning soft clay,
firing soft clay,
into hard, firm, erect Male Figure Sculpture.
I crawl from the foot of the bed
on hands and knees,
Round Female Sculpture.

She begins to open his trousers.

Ah Ah Ah.
Art is Pain.
I feel a hand over my face.

The man takes her chin and directs her down to his lap.
   She looks at his lap.

Aaaaaagh!
Man
   Squawking, Parrot?
   Seen nothing like it, Parrot?
   Different diet, Poll?
   How will you eat this chopped-about delicacy?
   What Art is needed here!
More Light Who did this to you?
Man (*takes hold of her*) Who did this to you?

48

SCENE THREE   RIBBONS OF COLOUR

*A lantern appears in the darkness. Lightens to reveal
Playful Kitten and Young Friend carrying their ribboned
sticks.*

Playful Kitten Down here.
Young Friend It's dark.
Playful Kitten I'm the one who holds the light.

  *They would both prefer to be the one who holds the
  light.*

  That's the river.
  It's poisonous but you can drink it
  if you like.
Young Friend No!
Playful Kitten Drink it!
Young Friend
  No!
  I drink blood!

  *This makes them laugh. Then scares them. They both
  would prefer to hold the lantern.*

Playful Kitten
  No!
  I'm the one who holds the light!
  We lie down here.

  They lie down on their backs.

  It happens when the lantern warms them.
  It takes a while.
Young Friend All right.
Playful Kitten (*pointing left*)
  There's where it's darkest.
  That's where Paa lives.

Young Friend
Oh.
Who's Paa?

Playful Kitten
My friend.
He's an animal really but he can talk.
I won't let him hurt you.

Young Friend What does he eat?

Playful Kitten
Dark.
He eats dark.
He chews it up and swallows it
and then he belches
and it makes light.

They giggle.

And then he farts
and it makes light.

They giggle some more.

And when he shits
he shits candles
and they're lit!

This is very funny.

And once he was sick
and it was a lantern!

This is even funnier.

You can kiss me.

Young Friend All right.

She does.

Playful Kitten You can touch me if you like.

Young Friend No, I don't want to.

Playful Kitten

All right.
You can hold my hand if you like.
Young Friend
All right.

They hold hands.

I don't like being touched.
Playful Kitten
I don't either really.
Not like that.
It's horrible really.
Young Friend
It's horrible.
Sister.
Playful Kitten
Sister.
Here they come.

Stars appear.

They're jewels really.
But they look like stars.
Young Friend I once found a star.
Playful Kitten Where?
Young Friend
In the grass.
It was green and sparkly.
Playful Kitten Did you keep it.
Young Friend
Yes.
But a robber stole it when I
was asleep.

They both play with their ribbons, swirling them in the air.

There's someone in the dark.
It's probably Paa.
Playful Kitten Probably.

She is not so sure.

Young Friend
He might have woken up and be
hungry.
Playful Kitten Yes.
Young Friend He might belch some light.

*A voice whispers from the dark: 'Playful Kitten . . .
Young Friend . . .'*

Playful Kitten Help . . .
Voice (*whispers*) Are you there?
Young Friend Yes, Paa . . .
Voice (*whispers*)
Come over here.
Bring the lantern.

*They go into the darkness with the lantern. It lights the
face of Rapture.*

Rapture (*hugging them and smacking them*)
Foolish! Foolish!
We thought we'd lost you!
Our sister is still behind the gates!
We are lost!
Bring the lantern!
How much light do you think we have!

She hurries them away.

SCENE FOUR   PERSPECTIVE

*Rapture arrives with Playful Kitten and Young Friend
among the ladies.*

Rapture
Here they are!

In the dark!
These two at least are here!
Scent-of-Ginger
Foolish girls!
Did you hear anything?
Did you see anyone?
Playful Kitten and **Young Friend**
No.
Nothing.
No one.
Playful Kitten Just the dark.
Sparkling Eyes Oh, misery!

She bursts into tears.

Love Mouth
More Light has not returned!
What has happened to her?
Oh, it is all awful!
Many Treasures
We are so low on . . . ingredients!
What is to be done?
Pure Joy A fine world!
Many Treasures
You were with her at the gates!
What happened, sister?
Pure Joy
She walked through the gates.
I closed them.

Silence.

I heard a scream.

Silence.

I came back to pose for Love Mouth.

There is nothing we can do!

There is nothing we can do!

Love's Gift We could go after her . . .

Pure Joy Why? Why? Why?

Shy Smile To save her, sister . . .

Many Treasures
And there is the matter of
eating . . .

Love's Gift We should go after her . . .

Pure Heart It would be only fair . . .

Pure Mind It would be only polite.

Scent-of-Ginger It would be dangerous . . .

Pure Joy
Dangerous?
Polite?
Fair?
We are in a tomb!
It is not the Emperor's any more!
It is ours!
We are dead already!
This is the world of Death!

Love Mouth
No! No! No!
I am painting!
We are all . . . making!
For the first time in my life . . .
it is . . . my life!
I am . . . creating!
Not Death!
No!
No!

Many Treasures
And we eat, sister.
We eat.
We are alive still.
We are alive!

Pure Joy

54

We are eating human flesh!
What will we *not* do?
Many Treasures
Nothing.
There is nothing we will not do now!
Nothing!

(*to others*) . . . Now, let us think
sensibly . . . What is to be done?

Shy Smile
It seems to me . . . excuse me . . .
there are three tasks to be accomplished.
Many Treasures Yes?
Shy Smile There is the getting of food.
Ladies Yes.
Shy Smile And the getting of our sister.
Ladies Yes.
Shy Smile And the getting on as normal . . .
Love Mouth Yes. Creating.
Pure Joy
As normal! Hahaha!
As normal!
Love's Gift
Some of us should see about the
getting of food and the getting
of our sister . . .
Shy Smile
The two tasks . . .
may be . . . may be one.
Ladies Ayeeee!

They contemplate this.

Many Treasures
So be it.
Who will go?

Show of hands.

Who will stay?

Show of hands.

So be it.

They look to Pure Joy. She has not raised her hand.

Pure Joy
Love Mouth paints.
Many Treasures cooks.
Makes music.
Playful Kitten dances.
I have made nothing yet.
Let me make a gesture.

She takes a bronze dagger and puts it to her heart.

Let me make a sacrifice.
Here I am. Meat.
Many Treasures
Sister, you have been meat long enough.
Be a woman with us.
Pure Joy
There is nothing worse than this!
Many Treasures Let us find out.
Pure Joy I'm frightened!

She drops the dagger.

Many Treasures You're hungry!

SCENE FIVE   FAUVISM

The middle gate. More Light and the Man.
   *They sit facing each other. Between them lie the sword
and the axe. They are playing scissors, paper, stone. She is*

scissors, he is scissors. He has never played before.

Man More Light?
More Light Yes.
Man More Light?

She is scissors, he is stone. He blunts her.

More Light
I was named for my quality.
The Emperor felt
when I entered a room
it became brighter.

He is paper, she is scissors. She cuts him.

Man And you played his games?
More Light He liked competitions.
Man Emperor's favourite?
More Light
At first.
But I read, listened.
My mind grew.
More light in it.
He turned to softer, more
flattering flames.

He is stone, she is paper. She wraps him.

Man You were sad?
More Light
I was glad.
My love for him was all Art.

She is paper, he is stone. She wraps him.

Man
Art don't work on me.
Practical me.
More Light Three. I win.

Man Then choose, More Light.

She takes the sword.
  She is stone, he is scissors. She blunts him.
  She is scissors, he is paper. She cuts him.
  She is paper, he is stone. She wraps him.

More Light Three.
Man Choose, More Light.

She puts the sword to his throat.

More Light Your Death.
  I choose your death.
Man
  Got hungry.
  Stole.
  Got caught.
  Got me balls chopped off.
  Dug a tomb.
  Got banged up in it.
  Whore stuck a sword in me gizzard.
  Did I live well!
  One last request.
More Light
  Of course.
  It would be only polite.
Man Make me happy.
More Light
  I can do nothing
  I say.
Man You can do this

He takes her hand, puts it to his cheek.

More Light
  He says
  and touches me so

58

He puts his hand to her cheek.

and so

She puts her other hand to his face

and so.

He puts his hand to her face.
    They look at each other.

I can do nothing for you
I say.
Man You can do this

He caresses her.

More Light
    he says
    and I touch him so
    and so and so.

She strokes his face, his hair.

Man Hurts . . . happiness,
More Light he says.
Man Worst pain . . . happiness,
More Light he says.
Man
    Makes ya think of the life
    ya wasted,
More Light he says.

She kisses him.

Man You using Art?
More Light I don't know.
Man Doesn't matter.
More Light
    It does
    I say.

He kisses her.
  From the darkness come Scent-of-Ginger, Pure Mind and Pure Heart. They leap upon him.

Ladies Excuse us . . . so sorry!

They hurl him to the ground.

Scent-of-Ginger Forgive us . . . we must hold you down!

They bind him fast.

Pure Mind and Pure Heart A thousand pardons . . . we
  must bind you tight!
Scent-of-Ginger Gag him! Excuse us . . . you must
  make   no sound!!!
Pure Heart
  What have you caught here, sister . . .
  a philosopher?
More Light Yes. A philosopher. Yes.
Pure Mind
  Our sisters guard the gates!
  We are hungry!
  Hurry!

They hurry the convict and More Light through the gates.

SCENE SIX   SCULPTURE

Love Mouth among the bronze army. She is alight with excitement.

Love Mouth
  I see it all now!
  The light had to be in my head!
  We must observe what has gone before!
  How things were done!
  We must see how the light in the

heads of our past masters struck
their space!
Of course!
By chipping and painting our friends
here . . . I destroy.
I take them into my head . . . transform
them with the light there . . .
the magnificent
correct
and knowledgeable play of
objects in light!
Yes?
Yes!
Yes! yes! yes!
I need something to make with!

The ambush party enters.

Scent-of-Ginger
    Here . . . here!
    If we bind him to this warrior he
    will be held fast!

They bind him.

Pure Mind and **Pure Heart**
    Excuse us . . . so sorry . . . just a little
    tighter. There!
Scent-of-Ginger More Light has lit our world again!
Pure Heart
    Scent-of-Ginger will make such
    music over this!

They hurry off.

Love Mouth
    More Light . . .
    I have got all the other ladies'
    likenesses in rough working form . . .

Would you be so kind . . . so gracious
as to spare me a short time for a
sitting?

More Light
I am to be painted?
Again?

Love Mouth
Sculptured!
Three-dimensional!
Beautiful object!

More Light
Of what material,
Love Mouth?

Love Mouth
Of clay!

She hurries her off.

SCENE SEVEN   PAA

*The convict is chained to the bronze warrior. He hears a
noise. A whispering.*
   Playful Kitten and Young Friend appear.

Playful Kitten Greetings, Paa.
Young Friend Greetings, Paa.
Playful Kitten
We have to touch him, or he can
escape.

Young Friend
All right.
You first.

Playful Kitten All right.

She goes to touch him. Runs back.

It's not frightening at all.

It is.

Now you.
Young Friend All right.

She goes to touch him. Runs back.

Now he can't get us.
Playful Kitten
No.
Never.
He's dead.
Young Friend Good.
Playful Kitten I'm hungry!

She runs out.

Young Friend
Bad Paa.
Don't . . .

She goes to stand right before him.

Don't ever do that again!

She smacks him.

Ever ever again!

She smacks him again and runs off.

SCENE EIGHT   A FEAST AT THE HOUSE OF LEVI

The ladies sit, thinking.
Many Treasures It is our world.
Ladies It is. Yes.
Many Treasures
No one but us can say what is right

and what is wrong.

Ladies No. No, they cannot.

Many Treasures
Therefore the decision is ours
alone.

Scent-of-Ginger We are all Emperors here!

Ladies Yes. Yes we are all Emperors
here.

Many Treasures So.

They think.

Shy Smile It is but a short step . . .

Love's Gift But a very short step . . .

Shy Smile
From eating the dead . . .
to . . . making someone dead . . .
in order to eat them.

Ladies Yes. Yes, a very short step.

Many Treasures And we are hungry.

Ladies
We are. Indeed we are.
Starving.

Pure Joy
I have never been so hungry
in all my life.
I am sick with it.

Ladies
Yes. Yes, indeed.
We are all sick with it.

Playful Kitten runs in.

Playful Kitten I am hungry.

Rapture Shush now. Shush.

Young Friend runs in.

Young Friend We should have a party!

Rapture Shush now. Shush.
Pure Joy
 We should have a party.
 Celebrate this . . . Empire
 we find ourselves in!
Ladies We should. Yes.
Shy Smile What else have we on?
Ladies Exactly!
Many Treasures
 We are back to the problem of . . .
 provisions.
Rapture
 We have just the one . . .
 source.
Shy Smile Which requires . . .
Ladies Attention.
Many Treasures Sisters, what is to be done?

 More Light and Love Mouth enter.

Pure Joy Sister, is your sword sharp?
Many Treasures We are preparing for a party!
Shy Smile
 Sister, the guest you brought back
 needs attention.
Love's Gift He must be prepared for the feast.
Ladies Our most important guest!
Many Treasures
 Here . . .

 She hands More Light the sword.

 prepare him, Sister.
More Light Why me?
Scent-of-Ginger
 When we came to help you, sister,
 You were in great danger
 for your lips touched his

65

and you were not bound.
A test.
We need this so.

More Light takes the sword and goes to leave. Pure Joy
catches her.

Pure Joy
Sister . . . if I may . . . I would be
pleased to perform this task
for you . . .

More Light
He has been cut about all
his life!
He is a man
but he is not a man!

Pure Joy
No one but you or I shall
know of this.
Give me the sword.
The deed is done.

More Light
How will you do this deed,
Pure Joy?

Pure Joy
I will take the sword so . . .
Find his heart so . . .
and with all my strength . . .
push.

More Light
You will leave him bound?
Leave in his gag?
Tied to a piece of the Emperor's Art?

Pure Joy
I am a lady of the Emperor, sister!
I cannot fence with him until he
drops!

More Light
    Why do you want to do this deed,
    Pure Joy?
Pure Joy
    I have done nothing.
    Ever.
    I am without Art!
More Light
    Pure Joy.
    You give pleasure.
    You are justly named.
    It is enough.
Pure Joy
    It has no heirs.
    It leaves no fortune.
    It does not survive.
More Light
    You remember Laughter . . .
    who died in childbirth . . .
    at the palace . . .
Pure Joy Yes.
More Light Her jokes?
Pure Joy Yes.
More Light When she dressed up as the Emperor?
Pure Joy Yes.
More Light
    Your face lights up.
    Your heart warms.
    She is dead.
    It is enough.
    Give me the sword.

SCENE NINE   THE IMPRESSIONIST

*More Light goes to the bronze army. She takes the gag out
of the convict's mouth. He spits in her face. She nods.*

Man Bitch.

More Light nods.

Bastard.
More Light
That, too.
Shall I cover your eyes?
Man
No, bitch.
I want to watch you at your work.
More Light So be it.

She lays the sword at his breast.

Any last requests?
Man
Listen to my song, Parrot.
We're digging out,
us lads.
We dug in . . . we can dig out.
Got the clever boys telling us where
to dig . . . using their most special minds to
fashion tools for us.
We're going to get out, Cage Bird,
What do you say to that?
More Light You're sure?
Man
I'm sure.
We're men.
We got brawn, we got brain.
Be out in the open very soon.

Going to be free.
Breathing fresh air.
Not this meat-filthy soup.
What do you say to that?
More Light Not you though.
Man
Less you let me go.
Less you and me slip away in the
dark like thieves in the night.
Take you with me.
Outside.
Fresh air.
Free.
Empire.
Gentle hill.
Red sun.
What do you say?
More Light I say . . .

She plunges the sword into him.

Die!
Man
Aaaaaagh!
Bitch!
Fool!
Bitch!
Why?
More Light
It would be no different!
For the Empire was his
and the gentle hill on which he stood
was his
and the red sun which lit the hill
was his!

He slumps.
  She holds him.

It is too late for us.
There would be no change.
Man
You daft bitch.
You'll never know.
Kiss me.

She does. He dies. She cradles him.
  The ladies come and take him away. More Light cries pitifully.

CHAPTER TEN   AN OBJECT PLACED IN ITS
ENVIRONMENT

Love Mouth enters carrying something covered in cloth.
Playful Kitten and Young Friend carry lanterns.

Love Mouth
Sister?
Sister . . . I have something to show you.
Put the lantern . . . there.
And that one . . . here.
And this . . . THE OBJECT . . . here.
I
More Light . . . look what I have made!

She takes off the cloth. It is a paper sculpture . . . quite small . . . of the ladies of the emperor.

See . . . it is us!
A bit rough . . . an early piece . . . but . . .
here is Playful Kitten . . .
and Young Friend . . .
Playful Kitten We're dancing!

70

Love Mouth
 Here is Many Treasures . . .
 stirring a pot of . . .
 Here's Rapture . . . Love's Gift . . .
 Fresh Morning . . . Sparkling Eyes . . .
 Scent-of-Ginger . . . Pure Joy, Pure Heart,
 Pure Mind arms about each other . . .
 Perfect Pleasure . . .
 Me . . . hands making . . .
 and look . . . look . . . who is this
 holding up a lantern?
More Light More Light?
Love Mouth More Light.
Young Friend I'm dancing!
More Light So you are.
Love Mouth
 I place it here,
 close to the bronze army
 but not of it, do you see?
 When, many years hence,
 people of the future gaze on this place
 they will say,
 'Aaah,
 Aaah . . . this is to do with this
 and this is to do with this.
 How very interesting Art is!'

SCENE ELEVEN A FESTIVAL OF ARTS

Music plays. Playful Kitten and Young Friend run off.
 A procession of the ladies enters, some playing. Playful Kitten and Young Friend are dancing. Other ladies bring on a steaming pot that smells of cooked meat.
 They take up the exact position of the small sculpture.

Love Mouth
   You see!
   You see?
   Exactly as we are!
   But for me with my hands in clay
   and you, More Light,
   holding the lantern!
Many Treasures Sisters . . . our feast.
Ladies
   We are hungry
   We are starving
   We are ravenous!
Scent-of-Ginger How good it smells!
Young Friend I'm so hungry!
Love Mouth
   I have deserved this!
   All this . . . creativity!
Pure Heart Have my seat, sister.
Pure Mind No, no, take mine!
Pure Joy My headache has quite gone!
Shy Smile
   I am getting quite used to this
   darkness.
   I see quite clearly!
Ladies
   Yes, yes!
   The eyes get used to it.
   One adjusts.
Rapture
   And one adjusts to the amount
   of air.
   It is quite fresh.
Ladies
   Yes, yes!
   It feels quite fresh!
   It feels like fresh air!

More Light looks up.

Shy Smile
One adjusts.
How miraculous the human body!

More Light stands.

More Light It is lighter.
Ladies One adjusts.
More Light It is cooler.
Ladies It feels like fresh air.
More Light
It is fresh air.
Listen!

Silence. Then a sound of digging.

TWELVE   THE TRANSFIGURATION

The ladies all become quite still.
   The light grows and grows from a central source high above. For the first time, natural daylight floods the tomb. A modern rope ladder drops into the centre of the space.
   A man, dressed in modern dress, descends. He looks around.

Modern Man (*soundlessly*) Christ!

A Woman in modern dress comes down the ladder. She stands with the Man. They look around.

Don't touch anything.

The Woman looks at him wordlessly.
   He goes to the bronze army.

Christ!

She kneels to look at the paper sculpture.

Modern Woman What's this?
Modern Man Don't touch anything.
Modern Woman This is falling to pieces . . . We must
be . . .

The Man finds the women of the court.

Modern Man Christ! Look at these!

The Woman goes to the ladies of the court.

Don't touch anything!
Modern Woman
Poor bastards!

*She reaches out to gently touch the face of More Light,
as the Man calls up the ladder.*

Modern Man
Get down here and have a look
at this lot!

*There is a sound of rustling and movement of old layers
of dust. From the ceiling flutter and drop millions and
millions of origami birds. The Modern Man and
Woman watch them silently as the lights fade.*
 Music.

Online Resources for Secondary Schools and Colleges

To support the use of Connections plays in the Drama studio and the English classroom, extensive resources are available exclusively online. The material aims not only to make the most of new technologies, but also to be accessible and easy to use.

Visit *www.connectionsplays.co.uk* for activities exploring each of the plays in a wide range of categories:

- Speaking and Listening
- Writing
- Reading and Response
- Practical Drama
- Plays in Production
- Themes

Carefully tailored tasks – whether for KS3, KS4 or A Level – are accompanied by clear learning objectives; National Curriculum links; ideas for extension and development, and for differentiation; Internet links; and assessment opportunities.

The material has been compiled by a team of practising English and Drama teachers, headed by Andy Kempe, author of *The GCSE Drama Coursebook* and (with Lionel Warner) *Starting with Scripts: Dramatic Literature for Key Stages 3 & 4*.

STANLEY
THORNES